Introduction

Having surfed the Web extensively since 1994, I am constantly amazed at the growing number of sites out there. Finding the best sites is not easy, so this book has been written to help you experience incredible things on the Net, without having to waste your precious time searching. Use this book and the Internet to learn, have fun and get things done.

Ken Leebow
Leebow@300INCREDIBLE.COM
http://www.300INCREDIBLE.COM

About the Author

Ken Leebow has been in the computer business for over 20 years. The Internet has fascinated him since he began exploring its riches a few years ago, and he has helped thousands of individuals and businesses understand and utilize its resources.

When not on the Net, you can find Ken playing tennis, running, reading or spending time with his family. He is living proof that being addicted to the Net doesn't mean giving up on the other pleasures of life.

— Dedication —

To my grandparents, Murray and Tillie Herman,
who have instilled in me a lifelong desire to question,
learn and experience the world.

300 More

Incredible Things to Do on the Internet

Volume II

300INCREDIBLE.COM, LLC
600 Village Trace, Building 23
Marietta, Georgia 30067

(800) 909-6505

ISBN 0-9658668-9-0

Acknowledgments

Putting a book together requires many expressions of appreciation. I do this with great joy, as there are several people who have played vital roles in the process:

- My kids, Alissa and Josh, who helped identify some of the cool sites.

- My wife, Denice, who has been patient with me while I have spent untold hours on the Internet.

- Paul Joffe and Janet Bolton, of *TBI Creative Services*, for their editing and graphics skills and for keeping me focused.

- The multitude of great people who have encouraged and assisted me via e-mail.

- Mark Krasner and Janice Caselli for sharing my vision of the book and helping make it a reality.

Books by Ken Leebow

300 Incredible Things to Do on the Internet • Volume I

300 More Incredible Things to Do on the Internet • Volume II

300 Incredible Things for Kids on the Internet

300 Incredible Things for Sports Fans on the Internet

300 Incredible Things for Golfers on the Internet

300 Incredible Things for Travelers on the Internet

300 Incredible Things for Health, Fitness & Diet on the Internet

300 Incredible Things for Auto Racing Fans on the Internet

300 Incredible Things for Self Help & Wellness on the Internet

America Online Web Site Directory
Where to Go for What You Need

1
<u>Smart Surfing</u>

http://www.flyswat.com

There are no insects at this site, but you'll find a lot to buzz about. As you surf, Flyswat's software turns key words of text into live, clickable links that lead to related Web resources.

2
<u>Help Me, Please!</u>

http://www.pcsupport.com

As computers have become more sophisticated, good support has never been more vital. Use this site to get help for your hardware and software problems.

3
<u>Computer History</u>

http://www.computerhistory.org

Though computers have dramatically changed our lives, they have not really been around for long. Learn about the history of computers from 1945 to the present.

4
<u>Computer Assistance</u>

http://www.myhelpdesk.com
The answers to your computer and software questions are just a click away.

5
<u>Serious Money</u>

http://www.ms-monopoly.com
This great parody is a Monopoly game that is Microsoft specific. Go ahead, click and have some fun.

6
<u>Dollar Bill</u>

http://www.microsoft.com/BillGates
http://www.usnews.com/usnews/nycu/tech/billgate/gatehigh.htm
Love him or not, Bill Gates has had a major impact on most of us. Here's his Web site, and—best of all—take a tour of his 66,000 square foot house.

7
Consult the Digital Goddess

http://www.komando.com
Kim Komando, self-proclaimed Digital Goddess, will assist with your computer and Internet concerns. She has a national radio show, a newsletter and many tips at her Web site.

8
The I Way

http://www.idrive.com
Computer data backups are important. How would you like to store some of your files on the Net? It's a great way to have off-site backups and access to your files from any Internet connection.

9
Virus Myths

http://kumite.com/myths
http://www.911virusalert.com
Tired of all those chain e-mail messages about viruses? These sites will let you know if a virus is real or a myth. Here's to your computer's good health.

10
I Got a Virus

http://www.mcafee.com
If you want to know more about viruses and how to get them out of your computer, visit this site.

11
History of the Net

http://www.isoc.org/internet-history
http://www.theatlantic.com/unbound/flashbks/computer/bushf.htm
Learn all about the origins and evolution of the Internet.

12
Speed it Up

http://computingcentral.msn.com/topics/bandwidth/speedtest50.asp
How fast is your Internet connection? Go to this site, and you'll know in a flash.

13
Neat Net Tricks

http://www.neatnettricks.com
Subscribe to this cool newsletter and you will receive tips about using the Net and your computer.

14
Gather 'Round the Net

http://www.myevents.com
http://www.myfamily.com
http://www.familypoint.com
In the old days, we would gather around the television. Now you can have your family members gather around this Web site. You can chat, store pictures, maintain a calendar and do other fun and creative things.

15
Family Friendly

http://www.ajkids.com
http://www.familyfriendlysearch.com
Need a search engine that kids can use? These sites meet the challenge.

16
Internet Stats

http://www.statmarket.com
http://www.mediametrix.com
These sites keep track of growth, trends and current news about the Net.

17
It's an E-World

http://www.e-commercetimes.com
http://www.zdnet.com/enterprise/e-business/bphome
http://www.nytimes.com/library/tech/99/09/biztech/technology
http://www.jeffbezosispersonoftheyear.time.com
Everyone's talking about e-commerce, and these sites offer in-depth information, including Amazon.com's Jeff Bezos, Time magazine's 1999 Person of the Year.

18
Net.com

http://www.internet.com
http://www.webopedia.com
Keep informed about Internet news. From stocks to resources, you'll find it here.

19
Powerful Rankings

http://www.gomezadvisors.com
http://powerrankings.forrester.com
Gomez and Forrester rank and rate various categories on the Net: travel, stock brokers, autos and other retail e-commerce sites.

20
From $2,100 to $0

http://www.creativegood.com
Here's an offer that seems too good to be true. Creative Good provides a seventy-five-page report about e-commerce for free. Normally, this report sells for $2,100, so hurry up and visit the site before the deal goes away.

21

The Internet Economy

http://www.thestandard.com
http://www.hotwired.com
http://www.interactiveweek.com
Are you fascinated by the stocks, technology and growth of the Internet economy?
These sites will keep you I-nformed.

22

High Tech Sites

http://www.techsightings.com
Get daily reviews of the best high-tech sites on the Net.

23
The New Economy

http://www.wired.com
http://www.upside.com
http://www.business2.com
http://www.redherring.com
http://www.fastcompany.com
These magazines offer help in understanding today's business and technology.

24
There's Gold Out There

http://www.strikingitrich.com
Everyone is wondering how to make money on the Net. Based on a book, this site discusses twenty-three Web sites that have done very well.

25
Auction Watch

http://www.auctionrover.com
http://www.auctionwatch.com
http://www.auctionbeagle.com
http://www.searchandfound.com
Everybody has the bidding bug, and everything is for sale. Use these sites to get in on the auction action.

26
Know Nolo

http://www.nolo.com
If it has to do with law, Nolo Press has written about it. From consumer issues to wills, you'll find complete information here—even a few lawyer jokes.

27
Take My Advice

http://www.freeadvice.com
To help people understand their rights, this site provides general information for more than one hundred legal topics.

28
Law and Order

http://www.courttv.com
You may not find Perry Mason here, but if you're a courtroom fanatic, you'll love all the information at this site.

29
Famous Trials

http://www.law.umkc.edu/faculty/projects/ftrials/ftrials.htm
Most of us are fascinated by important trials, and here are some of the most famous ones.

30
Your Real Audio Guide

http://www.realguide.com
One of the most exciting technologies on the Internet is RealAudio. This site will guide you to many of the fine audio and video sites.

31
Music While You Surf

http://music.lycos.com/radio
http://www.netradio.com
These music stations on the Net offer an incredible selection of songs, and every kind is covered.

32
Music for the Millennium

http://www.millennium.sonymusic.com
Our friends at Sony have compiled music from nearly 500 artists representing every genre. Sit back, relax and enjoy.

33
Everything Music

http://music.yahoo.com
http://www.ubl.com
Type in an artist, album or song, and you will be provided detailed information about your selection.

34
Yellow Submarine

http://www.hollywoodandvine.com/yellowsubmarine

Everyone can enjoy this site that celebrates the release of the remastered versions of the famous Beatles animated movie and music soundtrack.

35
Your Travel Guide

http://www.mytravelguide.com

Make this portal site one of your major destinations for travel plans.

36
May I Help You?

http://www.concierge.com

When traveling, this concierge can be your best guide to a city.

37
Travel Search Engines

http://www.exes.com
http://www.kasbah.com
As you plan your next trip, make sure you visit here for travel directories and search engines.

38
Travel Q&A

http://www.geocities.com/TheTropics/2442/database.html
Got questions? Arranged by geographic location, this is a database of people throughout the world who have the answers.

"You've been working too hard.
Instead of a heart beat, I'm getting a fax tone."

39
The Best and Lowest Fares

http://www.bestfares.com
http://www.lowestfare.com
http://www.lowairfare.com
http://www.air-fare.com
http://www.cheaptickets.com
Get the best possible prices on plane tickets by using these sites.

40
Cities A–Z

http://links.expedia.com
Click on a city, and you will find information about it here.

41
It's Grand

http://www.kaibab.org
The Grand Canyon is one of the great natural wonders of the world. If you can't get there, this site is a great substitute. Watch your step.

42
Cameras Around the World

http://www.earthcam.com
Can't get away today? See views from cameras in locations all over the world.

43
What's Your Orientation?

http://www.orientation.com
Here's a great portal site that focuses on information from six continents. Sorry, North America is not included.

44
Get Smart

http://www.selectsmart.com
This site will help you make decisions on such topics as politics, pets, health, food and more.

45
Decision Time

http://www.personalogic.com
Need help making a decision? Let this site be your guide.

46
What's Your Opinion?

http://www.epinions.com
http://www.productopia.com
http://www.exp.com
These folks have information on products and services, ranging from appliances to travel. If you need some advice, get an opinion here.

47
Personal Trainer

http://www.myprimetime.com
This is your "training" site for the subjects of home, money, work, health and play.

48
Hang on, Snoopy
http://www.snoopy.com
See the gang from Peanuts comics here.

49
Comics are Fun
http://www.comics.com
You'll find comics from Adam to Ziggy at this comic depot.

50
Meet the Joke Jester
http://shadow.ieor.berkeley.edu/humor
Get some great jokes that are geared especially to your taste. Rate a few with the jester, and he will continue to provide you with jokes that you enjoy.

51
Elusive Illusions

http://www.illusionworks.com
http://www.sandlotscience.com
Is it real, or is it an illusion? Spend a few moments here for some scientific fun.

52
Best of What's New

http://www.popsci.com/features/bown/bown99
Popular Science lists the one hundred best achievements in science and technology.

53
Living with Technology

http://www.technocopia.com
Is technology taking over your life? This site discusses its effects at home, at work and at play.

54
Science Online

http://www.scitechdaily.com
http://www.sciencedaily.com
http://www.scienceagogo.com
It's educational, fun and even interesting. Here, you can read many timely stories about science.

55
The Final Frontier

http://www.space.com
http://www.spaceref.com
http://www.spacestation.com
These sites are the next best things to being out there.

56
Shop Safely

http://www.safeshopping.org
http://www.bbb.org/library/shoponline.html
The Internet is the world's largest mall. These sites should help you become a more knowledgeable consumer.

57
Catalogs and More

http://www.catalogcity.com
http://www.catalogsite.com
http://www.bluefly.com
http://www.shoponline123.com
http://www.wiworksmainstreet.com
Are you a catalog or outlet mall shopper? Check them all out on the Net.

58
Professional Bargain Shopper

http://www.dealtime.com
http://www.mysimon.com
http://www.pricewatch.com
http://www.pricescan.com
http://www.jango.com
http://www.shopfind.com
http://www.bottomdollar.com

Wouldn't it be great to have your very own personal shopper who knows exactly where to get the best deals? Here are some good ones, and you don't have to pay for the service.

59
Gift Certificate

http://www.giftcertificates.com
Send someone a gift certificate from one of many name brand companies.

60
Great Values

http://www.valpak.com
http://www.valupage.com
http://www.supercoups.com
http://www.mycoupons.com
http://www.coolsavings.com
If you're a coupon clipper, you'll love getting these coupons on the Net.

61
Dollar Stretcher

http://www.stretcher.com
This site's motto is "live better for less." Just about anything you can spend a buck on is discussed here.

62
Offline Sales

http://www.shoppinglist.com
Where are the sales and good deals in the "bricks and mortar" world of the stores? Pop in your zip code, and you'll know where the sales are.

63
Shop Bot

http://www.dealpilot.com
Type in a title of a movie, book or CD, and you will get a detailed list of prices from many online stores.

64
I Wish

http://www.ohiwish.com
http://www.uwish.com
http://www.wishbox.com
http://www.kidswish.com
Let these sites assist in the gift giving and receiving process.

65
Smart Consumer

http://www.bizrate.com
http://www.esmarts.com
Be a sharp consumer. These sites offer information, Web sites and a weekly newsletter with various shopping categories.

66
Dare to Compare

http://www.comparenet.com
http://www.thebigcompare.com
http://www.consumerreview.com
Before you make a purchase, get unbiased information from these buyer's guides.

67
Shopping With a Cause

http://www.greatergood.com
Greatergood allows you to shop online and have a portion of the proceeds go to a charitable cause.

68
Credit Cards

http://www.cardweb.com
If you must use plastic for purchases, visit Cardweb first.

69
Hey Big Spender

http://www.luxuryfinder.com
If you've got big bucks, visit the luxury finder site and spend away.

70
I Wanna Be Free

http://www.4freestuff.com
http://www.freeshop.com
http://www.freemania.net
http://www.weeklyfreebie.com
http://www.100percentfreestuff.com
Who said nothing is free? Visit these sites to see all that is available.

71
Personal Digital Assistant

http://www.mypdanews.com
If you have a PDA or are thinking of getting one, you can acquire all your news and
information here.

72
Biography 101

http://members.home.net/klanxner/lives

If your bookshelf is filled with biographies, you'll enjoy this professional collection of biographical Web sites.

73
Influential Folks

http://www.pathfinder.com/time/time100

Time magazine has covered most of the influential people of the 20th century at this site.

74
What a Century

http://www.thecentury.com

Well, the 1900s are over and we've survived the onset of Y2K. Now is a good time to take a look back at the past 100 years.

75
Those Were the Days

http://scriptorium.lib.duke.edu/adaccess
http://www.lib.virginia.edu/exhibits/sixties
http://www.britannica.com/psychedelic
http://wallofsound.go.com/features/stories/top_100_albums
Relive the decades of the 60s, 70s, 80s and 90s.

76
Get Your Kicks

http://www.route66.com
Ever miss the good old days—before Interstate Highways? Go cruisin' down Route 66.

77
Look Up!

http://www.dccomics.com/radio
It's a bird…it's a plane…it's Superman! Listen to the original radio broadcasts of our favorite superhero.

78
Let's Talk

http://www.talkway.com
http://www.chatlist.com
Newsgroups and chatting on the Net can be informative and fun. These sites offer targeted interest groups to you. At Chatlist, check out the section for acronyms and smilies.

79
Remarkable Discussions

http://www.remarq.com
The Internet has created a huge number of discussion communities, and this site offers groups in most major categories. Go ahead and join the conversation.

"My team is developing the world's greatest search engine. We've used it to find Kate's contact lens, Larry's ambition, and your hair!"

80
Lots of Topics

http://www.topica.com
http://www.fidget.com
http://www.webscoutlists.com
http://www.meer.net/~johnl/e-zine-list
Every interest group under the sun can be found here. Subscribe to a newsletter of interest to you.

81
Log Off!

http://www.netaddiction.com
http://www.netaddiction.com/resources/test.htm
Are you spending too much time on the Net? Take the test and get some advice.

82
Reading is Fun

http://www.bookspot.com
This is the spot to find many great resources related to reading.

83
Book It!

http://www.bookradio.com
If you like reading, then I'm sure you'll love listening to these author interviews.

84
Celebrity Read

http://www.gpl.lib.me.us/wrwind.htm
I don't know how they find the time, but these well-known people apparently read lots of good books.

85
Long Distance for Free

http://www.dialpad.com
Sign up with Dialpad, and you can make your long-distance calls for free on the Net. You can even reach out and touch someone who is not on the Internet.

86
Fax for Free

http://www.fax4free.com
Send a fax on the Net; it's simple and it's free. You can even fax someone a word processing file.

87
Ring, Ring, Ring

http://www.mrwakeup.com
Wake up calls, reminders, stock market updates and more, this service will call you with the information you requested.

88
The Name Game

http://www.zelo.com
What does your name mean? Type it in, and instantly learn its origin and meaning.

89
Postage.com

http://www.stamps.com
http://www.estamp.com

Tired of waiting in long lines at the post office? Finally, you can use your computer as a postage meter. Download some software, and you'll be ready to go.

90
Track Any Package

http://www.packtrack.com

Here's a simple site that allows you to track a package sent through the major delivery services. If you do a lot of shipping, you should place this one on your browser toolbar.

91
Simple Calculations

http://www.moneyopolis.org/calc.asp

In life, the simplest things are often the best. Here's a calculator that's easy to use, and you can place it on your toolbar.

92
This Does Compute

http://www.calculator.com
http://www.calcbuilder.com
You won't believe the wide variety of online calculators that are available to you at these sites.

93
Meet the Wizard

http://www.thewizardofodds.com
Bet you'll be a better gambler after visiting this site.

94
News Junky

http://www.listentothenews.com
If you love the news, this is a site you will want to tune in. From NPR to Iranian radio and special topics, you can spend hours listening to all types of news.

95
Your News Outlet

http://www.newshub.com

In one location, receive timely news stories from many of the finest publications on the Net. You can even customize the site for your own needs.

96
Media Information

http://www.mediagossip.com

Read about interesting news stories from major publications.

97
Here on the Web

http://www.hereontheweb.com

What's happening? What timely topic or issue do you want to know about? It's all here on the Web.

98
Headline News

http://www.7am.com
http://www.1stheadlines.com
Browse the headlines, and get your news quickly and easily at these sites.

99
MyNewspaper.com

http://www.crayon.net
Create your own newspaper. However, you'll have to provide your own coffee.

100
Newsmakers Online

http://cnn.com/resources/newsmakers
Learn from CNN profiles about people in the news.

101
Be an Individual

http://www.individual.com
These folks have been around awhile, providing customizable news and information.

102
Money Makes the World Go 'Round

http://www.cnbc.com
http://www.on24.com
http://www.money.net
http://www.thomsoninvest.net
http://www.multexinvestor.com

Are you addicted to stock reporting? Let these sites link you to the markets.

103
Investor's Chat

http://www.investorschat.com
http://www.investingonline.org

Investment chat rooms and online investing have become unbelievably popular. Test these sites out to see if online investing is your cup of tea.

104
He's a 10K Wizard

http://www.10kwizard.com

10K Wizard's market-leading, proprietary search technology lets users view SEC filings of more than 68,000 companies and search historical filings—from the start date of each company's existence—by key words, phrases and names.

105
Book It

http://www.quicken.com

Quicken takes care of your bookkeeping and will help keep you fiscally sound on the Net. It has major categories that include investing, mortgage, insurance, taxes, banking and retirement.

106
Tools of the Trade

http://www.inc.com/tools

If you're in the business world, you will want to take advantage of Inc. magazine's business tools.

107
Be an Insider

http://www.insidertrader.com
http://www.individualinvestor.com
Pop in a stock symbol and identify the insiders who own that stock.

108
Play the Market

http://www.smg2000.org
The Stock Market Game enables participants to discover the risks and rewards involved in decision-making, the sources and uses of capital and other related economic concepts.

109
Stock Tips

http://www.bigtipper.com
Hey, have I got a tip for you! Get some stock advice from these experts.

110
Let's Get Technical

http://www.clearstation.com
This site claims to be "for the intelligent investment community."

111
Play the Market

http://www.marketplayer.com
http://www.marketguide.com
Build and test your stock market strategy. For assistance while playing the market, check out the guide.

112
Companies Online

http://www.companiesonline.com
Get information on over 100,000 companies.

113
World Economy

http://www.worldlyinvestor.com
We're in a world economy, so here's a site dedicated to international investing.

114
Mutual Funds

http://www.findafund.com
http://www.fundalarm.com
http://www.fundsinteractive.com
The easiest way to get into the market is via mutual funds. Let these sites help you become a knowledgeable investor.

115
Financial Reporting

http://www.worth.com
http://www.barrons.com
http://www.economist.com
http://www.bloomberg.com
http://www.kiplinger.com
Some of the best financial reporting offline is also on the Net.

116
Your Path to Money

http://www.pathfinder.com/money
Money magazine provides this comprehensive financial site.

117
Give Peace a Chance

http://www.financialpeace.com
If you are committed to becoming financially secure, listen to Dave Ramsey's daily radio broadcast.

"I've grossed over two million dollars since
I started advertising my business on the Internet!"

118
You Look Like a Million

http://www.armchairmillionaire.com
A million bucks just ain't what it used to be, but it's still not bad. Get simple and practical advice here.

119
Wealth Meter

http://www.cnetinvestor.com/ceometer/ceometer.asp
We're obsessed with the earnings of the super rich. At this interactive site, find out which billionaires made or lost money today.

120
Wall Street

http://www.wsrn.com
http://www.123jump.com
If you need information about a stock, jump over to these sites.

121
How's Your Credit?

http://www.qspace.com
http://www.equifax.lycos.com
Obtain your personal credit rating, and find other useful financial tools here.

122
Darwin Awards

http://www.darwinawards.com
Recognized posthumously, these award winners have done some strange things and have not lived to talk about them.

123
Sports Search

http://www.sportsearch.com
http://sports.profusion.com
http://www.sportssleuth.com
If you love sports, search to your heart's content.

124
It's a Hit

http://www.sporthits.com
Here's a great site to quickly get to the major sports.

125
The Best of...

http://www.baseball-links.com
http://www.nflhistory.com
http://www.nationwide.net/~patricia
http://www.inthecrease.com
http://www.golfonline.com
...baseball, football, basketball, hockey and golf.

126
Baseball Stats

http://baseball.ibi.com
Baseball has a wealth of statistics, and this site will keep the baseball fanatic busy for a while.

127
National Pastime

http://www.baseball-almanac.com
If you love baseball, check out the almanac. Spend a few moments here, and learn some interesting things about the game you love.

128
It's the Equipment

http://www.golfweb.com/equipment/proreport/index.html
Golfers love getting new clubs. Before you buy your next set, find out what the winning pros are using. See you on the tour.

129
Be in the Zone

http://www.wrestlezone.com
This site's slogan is "give me wrestling or give me death." Yes, the Internet does have something for everyone.

130
Tomorrow's Leaders

http://www.thinkquest.org

There's a lot of talk today about "the poor education our children are getting." Go to this site for a different view.

131
The Knowledge Portal

http://www.hungryminds.com

The more I know, the more I know that I don't know. Get educated by signing up for some courses on the Net.

132
Teacher's Resource

http://www.pbs.org/teachersource

http://www.teachersfirst.com

Though primarily designed for teachers, we can all learn things from these sites.

133
Encyclopedias Online
http://www.britannica.com
http://www.funkandwagnalls.com
Remember the good old days of encyclopedias — twenty volumes and tons of information? The information is still there, but now it's online.

134
3D Thesaurus
http://www.plumbdesign.com/thesaurus
Type a word and click on the words that are displayed. Follow a thread of meaning, and create a spatial map of linguistic associations. Try it out, it's cool.

135
A Web of...
http://www.facstaff.bucknell.edu/rbeard/diction.html
...online dictionaries.

136
How's Your Vocabulary?

http://www.voycabulary.com
This interesting and amazing tool will link every major word at a given Web site to a dictionary or Thesaurus.

137
Big Words in the News

http://www.mcs.net/~kvj/spizz.html
How's your vocabulary? Look at a list of unusual words that have appeared in recent news articles, and try to guess the definitions.

138
Vocabulary Builder

http://www.wordsmith.org/awad/index.html
Want to sound smart? Use the words that this wordsmith will e-mail to you each and every day.

139
Quoteland

http://www.quoteland.com
http://quoteworld.eilc.org
http://www.quotations.co.uk
Ah, a profound quote. Many of life's truths come from these quotations.

140
WOW

http://www.wisdom.com
Words of Wisdom will e-mail a daily profound quote to you.

141
Portal to War

http://www.wtj.com/portal
Here's a military resource for researchers, hobbyists, military professionals and all others with an interest in military history, science and defense.

142
Empowerment for All

http://www.wemedia.com

This site's stated mission is "to empower persons with disabilities, their families and friends by being a conduit for education, knowledge, technology, entertainment and numerous other services in an exciting, convenient and accessible fashion."

143
Incredible People

http://etext.virginia.edu/jefferson
http://www.westegg.com/einstein
http://www.pathfinder.com/time/time100/poc/home.html
http://edison.rutgers.edu

Thomas Jefferson, Albert Einstein and Thomas Edison are three people who have truly made a difference.

144
Incredible Library

http://lcweb2.loc.gov

The Library of Congress has an enormous collection, with over sixty exhibits online and many more on the way. The "Today in History" section treats you to a different historical document every day.

145
Got a Question?

http://www.xpertsite.com
http://www.allexperts.com
http://www.expertcentral.com

These experts will probably have the answer.

146
There's No Such Thing...

http://www.looksmart.com/live

...as a dumb question, and the folks at Looksmart will answer one of yours within twenty-four hours.

147
Ray's Trivia Page
http://www.primate.wisc.edu/people/hamel/trivia.html
If it has to do with trivia, Ray knows about it.

148
Did You Know?
http://www.didjaknow.com/archive.html
Spend some time here to learn an interesting fact or piece of trivia.

149
Twenty Questions
http://come.to/20Q
Remember the game Twenty Questions? In this version, the computer asks the questions in an attempt to guess what you are thinking. I finally gave up after it beat me twice!

150
It's a Fact

http://www.cool-fact.com/archive
Peruse these archives of interesting facts. It's guaranteed to make you feel more knowledgeable.

151
Fighting Ignorance...

http://www.straightdope.com
...since 1973, columnist Cecil Adams—self-proclaimed World's Smartest Human Being—provides "all worthwhile human knowledge" on a variety of topics.

152
Think Tank

http://www.upi.com/corp/links/think.shtml
Unlimited ideas and possibilities come from these think tanks.

153
Common Genius
http://www.prolificus.com
The primary goal of Prolificus is to make you aware of the vast potential within your mind and to persuade you to take an interest in improving it.

154
Smart Alec
http://www.mensa.org/workout.html
Think you're pretty smart? Head on over to the MENSA Web site and take the test. Good luck.

155
Be Creative
http://www.bemorecreative.com
Spend a couple of hours here, and you might learn how to become more creative.

156
Curious?

http://www.didyouknow.com
http://www.factcat.com
Do you ask a lot of questions? Then check out these sites for a lot of answers.

157
Animal Farm

http://www.acmepet.com
http://www.animalfair.com
http://www.petplanet.com
http://www.petstation.com
http://www.animalnetwork.com
Pets make great family members. If you already have a pet, or are considering one, these sites will be great resources.

158
Puppy Watch

http://www.thepuppycam.com
Visit puppy cam, and view one of thousands of dogs that can be adopted.

159
Greetings

http://www.greetst.com
http://mypostcards.net
http://www.postcards.org
http://www.hallmark.com
http://www.cardmaster.com
http://www.bluemountain.com
E-mail cards are very popular on the Net. Here are some great sites for sending any type of greeting card.

160
Greetings with Music

http://greetings.mp3.com
MP3 is a hot technology on the Net. Now you can send a card along with music.

"Our palm-top computer is available with many options,
including the nose-top printer, scanner hat,
and 100MB removable storage socks!"

161
MP3

http://broadcast.go.com/MP3
http://www.pathfinder.com/time/digital/reports/mp3/index.html
http://www.musicmatch.com
http://www.4mp3audio.com

Though it actually stands for "Motion Picture Experts Group Audio Layer 3," this revolutionary music technology is much more. Learn all about it, and make your computer into a virtual jukebox.

162
RSVP, Please

http://www.evite.com
http://www.eparties.com
http://www.seeuthere.com

Are you having a party? Use one of these sites to invite your guests.

163
Time Capsule
http://dmarie.com/asp/history.asp
Celebrating someone's birthday? Bring this time capsule with you.

164
Flower Power
http://www.proflowers.com
http://www.1800flowers.com
Flowers always brighten up a room. Here are some companies who will be happy to send them on a regular basis.

165
Virtual Flowers
http://www.flowernetwork.com/virtual-b
Send e-flowers to someone you love. These may not smell as good as the real thing, but they're free and will last longer.

166
Feelin' All Right

http://www.aromaweb.com

Aromatherapy is the use of volatile plant oils—including essential oils—to achieve psychological and physical well being.

167
Everything But The Kitchen Sink

http://www.kitchenlink.com

http://www.recipecenter.com

http://www.foodtv.com

If it has to do with food, cooking, recipes or the kitchen, you'll find it here.

168
Food on the Web

http://www.foodweb.com

http://www.restaurantreport.com/Top100

These sites concentrate on food, dining and the good life.

169
Big Tipper

http://www.tipping.org

Become an educated tipper. Here's to great service.

170
Rating Restaurants

http://www.trabble.com

This site asks you to rate a few restaurants, and it will then recommend where it thinks you should eat.

171
Matchmaker, Matchmaker...

http://www.match.com

If Yenta knew about this dating site, she'd be singing, "the times, they are a changin'."

172
It Takes a Village

http://www.ivillage.com
http://www.women.com
http://my.women.com
http://www.womenconnect.com

These villages are designed for women. From beauty to working at home, you'll find it all here.

173
List Mania

http://www.statejobs.com/list.html
http://gwis2.circ.gwu.edu/~gprice/listof.htm

Do you love lists? You'll find more here than you ever wanted.

174
Wanted!
http://www.fbi.gov/mostwant/topten/tenlist.htm
http://www.amw.com
http://www.mostwanted.org
Here are the lists of the FBI's Ten Most Wanted, America's Most Wanted and the World's Most Wanted.

175
All Points Bulletin
http://www.apbnews.com
Do you like watching your local evening news? If you do, you'll enjoy this site devoted exclusively to crime, justice and safety.

176
Business Information
http://www.infousa.com
Here's a site designed for small business owners, entrepreneurs and sales and marketing executives. Everyone can find some good information at this site.

177
Small Business Information

http://www.bizmove.com
Here is a complete resource of small business information that is packed with guidelines and tools to successfully manage your business.

178
Business to Business

http://www.bizbuyer.com
There's a lot of focus on business-to-business transactions on the Net. This site matches small businesses with vendors.

179
Let's Talk Business

http://www.ltbn.com
http://www.entrepreneurmag.com
It seems like everyone is trying to be an entrepreneur. If you qualify, these sites will help you get where you need to go.

180
What's Your Opinion?

http://www.gallup.com
Since 1935, Gallup has been polling opinions on almost every subject. I think that 99% of those who visit this site will enjoy it.

181
Stuffing the Ballot Box

http://www.thebigballot.com
At BigBallot, you can vote your opinion on a variety of issues ranging from current news to sports.

182
Magazine Newsstand

http://www.magazine-rack.com
Want to read a magazine? This newsstand lists many popular ones by category.

183
Upscale Magazines

http://www.theatlantic.com
http://www.harpers.org
Though Harper's content is not actually online, click on "Harper's Index" and you will be propelled to hundreds of interesting statistics.

184
The S-Word

http://www.slate.com
http://www.salon.com
Slate and Salon are two thought-provoking, online publications that will entertain and move you.

185
Join the Festivities

http://www.festivals.com
http://www.festivalfinder.com
From art to sports, you'll have a great time researching these festivals.

186
Poli-Sci

http://www.politics.com
http://politics.yahoo.com
http://www.opensecrets.org
http://www.e-thepeople.com
http://www.usademocracy.com
http://www.freedomchannel.com
http://www.campaignline.com/odds
Keep up with campaigns and other political developments through these sites.

187
It's Official

http://www.algore2000.com
http://www.billbradley.com
http://www.georgewbush.com
http://www.mccain2000.com
http://cnn.com/ELECTION/2000
Visit the major 2000 Presidential candidates' official Web sites, and follow the election process with CNN.

188
Let's Party

http://www.rnc.org
http://www.democrats.org
http://www.reformparty.org
See the official Web sites for the Republican, Democrat and Reform parties.

189
Electoral College

http://www.jump.net/~jnhtx/ec/ec.html
Every four years, we hear a lot about the Electoral College. This site allows you to "play" with the electoral process. Pick a winner in each state and see what happens.

190
Smart Voter

http://www.vote-smart.org
http://www.congress.org
Track the performance of over 13,000 political leaders, and write your congressman at congress.org.

191
Gone Forever

http://www.politicalgraveyard.com
Our politicians have taxed us to death. Now, thanks to Lawrence Kestenbaum, you will know the final resting places of over 30,000 politicians.

192
History of Presidential Elections

http://www.multied.com/elections
From 1789 to 1996, you'll find interesting election information and results.

193
Seconds to Live

http://www.deathclock.com
How much time do you have left? This site estimates your life span and shows it to you as a timer counting down the seconds. You can even make this your screensaver.

194
Death and…

http://www.taxprophet.com
http://www.tax.org/Quotes/quotations.htm
…taxes. These sites provide advice and some funny quotes about taxes. What could possibly be funny about taxes?

195
Safe Listening

http://www.broadcast.com/simuflite
http://www.policescanner.com/police.stm
Listen to live conversations between air traffic controllers and pilots. When you've heard enough of that, tune in to see what the police are up to.

196
Calendars Can Be Fun

http://www.timeanddate.com
http://www.webexhibits.com/calendars
Here are a couple of sites that will teach you about time and calendars. You can also compute the time between dates, such as how many days until the birth of the baby.

"Do you MIND?!"

197
Time Management

http://www.when.com
http://www.anyday.com
http://calendar.yahoo.com
http://www.digital.daytimer.com
The time has come to use calendars and "to do" lists on the Net. You can even display your schedule to people on the Web.

198
Remind Me, Please

http://www.lifeminders.com
http://www.candor.com/reminder
Are you forgetful about some of your commitments? These sites will be happy to help you remember.

199
Time

http://www.timedance.com
Timedance allows people to schedule their time and events online. Got some folks who need to communicate and coordinate? This might be the best solution.

200
Arcade City

http://www.freearcade.com
Kill some time by playing games at this free arcade.

201
Playtime

http://www.zone.com
You should have lots of fun playing these games.

202
Isn't Life Strange?

http://www.theweirdsite.com
People and the Internet can both be very bizarre. Check out some of these odd things at this site.

203
This is Stupid!

http://www.dumblaws.com
In my hometown, it is illegal to spit from a car or bus, but citizens may do so from a truck. Check out dumb laws in your area.

204
Urban Legend Has It…

http://www.snopes.com
http://www.urbanlegends.com
…that most of these often-told stories are actually untrue! Legends spread even faster on the Net, but these sites might help debunk a few for you.

205
It Must Be True

http://www.thisistrue.com

"A man sued his doctor because he survived his cancer longer than the doctor predicted." Find out about all kinds of such items that are strange, but true.

206
When the Sky Fell

http://www.disasterium.com

At The Living Almanac of Disasters, click on any day of the yearly calendar and see what calamities occurred on that date in history. You can even do a separate search for fires, earthquakes and transportation catastrophes.

207
Spoof it Up

http://www.theonion.com

http://www.wackytimes.com

With all the bad news floating around the world, we need more sites like this. They are guaranteed to make you laugh.

208
Off the Wall

http://www.nationallampoon.com
It's fun, it's goofy, it's spoofy and totally graphic. Sit back, relax and don't fall off your chair while laughing.

209
Letters from Bill

http://www.cranial.com/hertes.html
William Hertes has an interesting hobby. He sends odd letters to corporations, and these companies usually reply. At this site, Bill shares some of these hilarious letters with us.

210
"Let There Be Fun"

http://www.uproar.com
That's the motto at this site. There are many quizzes for you to take, so pick a category, and let the fun begin!

211
Quiz Me

http://www.quizsite.com
Discover lots of fun quizzes here. You can select subject area and level of difficulty.

212
Crossword Puzzles

http://www.dailycrossword.com
http://www.mentalstate.com
http://www.student.com/feature/xwords
http://www.oneacross.com
http://www.ojohaven.com/fun/crossword.html
Get your keyboard in hand, and prepare to solve these puzzles. If you need some help with a word, try the last two sites.

213
Putting the Pieces Together

http://www.jigzone.com
Jigsaw puzzle fans will love this site. Choose from hundreds of puzzles of all degrees of difficulty. Move the pieces with your mouse, time yourself and—if you get stuck—tell it to solve itself.

214
Browser Watch

http://browserwatch.internet.com
What's the latest with Internet browsers? Browse this site to find out.

215
What If . . .

http://www.myesp.com
http://www.gooey.com
. . . everyone searching the Web for the same thing at the same time could talk to each other? That would be incredible! Leave it to someone on the Net to figure this one out.

216
Top 50

http://50.lycos.com

What are people searching for? Lycos knows and tells here. It's a good window into pop culture.

217
It's All 4 You

http://www.4anything.com

The name says it best; "4 anything" on the Net, you should visit here.

218
Internet Robot

http://www.botspot.com

On the Net, there are robots that are happy to do the searching for you. This site lists the best of the "bots."

219
Search Engine Watch

http://www.searchenginewatch.com
http://www.notess.com/search
These sites are designed for serious searchers, Webmasters, marketers and others who love search engines.

220
Search A to Z

http://search.cnet.com/Alpha
http://www.searchenginesgalore.com
http://www.searchability.com
There are search engines for every topic available here.

221
Fast Search

http://www.google.com
http://www.alltheweb.com
http://www.allonesearch.com
The Web is getting huge, and we need fast, efficient tools to find things. Here are some search engines that are ready for the task.

222
Top Search Engines

http://www.av.com
http://www.yahoo.com
http://www.lycos.com
http://www.excite.com
http://www.askjeeves.com
If you have a search to do, these are some search engines you will want to use.

223
All About the Net

http://azlist.about.com
The folks from About.com have more than 600 guides to point you in the right direction on the Net. There is a listing of all the guide topics in alphabetical order, so you'll never be lost again.

224
International Search Engines

http://www.searchenginecolossus.com
Join the World Wide Web and go international. This site has search engines for every country.

225
World Wide Phone Numbers

http://www.phonenumbers.net
From Argentina to Zimbabwe, you'll have telephone numbers at your fingertips.

Wallingford ct

226
Find Me

http://www.search-shark.com

http://members.aa.net/~flip/search/search.html

If someone can be found, this shark will put the bite on him.

227
Business Search Engine

http://pinstripe.opentext.com

Here's a search engine that has business people in mind.

228
I Need a Guide

http://www.netguide.com

NetGuide has been around for a long time, and its directory will guide you to many fine things on the Net. Make sure you sign up for the weekly e-mail newsletter.

229
Be Anonymous

http://www.anonymizer.com
http://www.enonymous.com
Web sites can track you while you surf. Find out how to surf anonymously, and learn a lot about privacy issues on the Net.

230
Document This

http://www.lib.umich.edu/libhome/Documents.center/webdirec.html
The University of Michigan has an A-to-Z listing of documents and Web sites. Spend a rainy day here.

231
Statistical Rolodex

http://www.cdc.gov/nchs/fastats/fastats.htm
The National Center for Health Statistics provides a very comprehensive index of interesting information.

232
Health Online

http://www.stayhealthy.com
http://www.healthology.com
http://www.personalmd.com
http://www3.bc.sympatico.ca/me/patientsguide
Your health is your most valuable asset. Use these sites to assist in maintaining a healthy lifestyle.

233
Medication Bible

http://www.drugdigest.org
Learn about medications, drug interactions and more at this drug site.

234
School Reporting

http://www.theschoolreport.com
An amazing source for statistics about SAT scores by high schools, this site also has all kinds of other information.

235
The Weather Plan...

http://www.weatherplanner.com
http://inbox.weather.com
http://www.intellicast.com
... for the weather fan.

236
Teens Online

http://www.bolt.com
Everything teenagers discuss is here—well, almost everything.

237
Pop Goes the...

http://www.pimpleportal.com
... pimple! You've got to love a site that is dedicated to a teen's worst nightmare.

"Do you, Jason, take Heather to have and to hold,
to e-mail and to fax, to page and to beep,
until death do you part?"

238
How Do You Do That?

http://www.how2.com
Learn how to do things that relate to home, work, shopping and play. You'll find tutorials, discussions and more.

239
Learn How

http://www.ehow.com
From autos to travel, you'll learn how to do almost everything.

240
Home 101

http://www.ahahome.com
http://www.homearts.com
http://www.hgtv.com
Everything you ever needed to know about home ownership and maintenance can be found here.

241
Use It

http://www.wackyuses.com
Learn how to use everyday products in unusual, helpful ways. To clean a toilet, for example, drop in two Alka-Seltzer tablets, wait twenty minutes, brush and flush.

242
Having a Baby

http://www.childbirth.org
http://www.babynamer.com
http://www.babyzone.com
http://www.babysoon.com
http://www.abcparenting.com
http://www.parentgarden.com
http://www.softgreetings.com
Get ready for the roller coaster ride of parenthood. And don't forget to send the baby announcement to all your friends and family through softgreetings.com.

243
Heeeelp!

http://www.disciplinehelp.com
If you need a little help with your child, go to this site for over 100 tips.

244
Can We Talk?

http://www.talkingwithkids.org
No one ever said parenting would be easy. Use this site's "10 tips for talking with kids about tough issues" as a starting point.

245
The Latest Craze

http://www.pokemon.com
http://www.pokemontop50.com
It's colorful, and it's unbelievably popular with kids. If you have no idea what Pokémon is, visit here to find out. And if you're a collector, indulge your passion at these sites.

246
My Movie Critic

http://www.moviecritic.com
http://www.cinemascore.com
Give your opinion about some movies, and then let the Movie Critic go to work for you. These sites will suggest other movies that you will probably like.

247
Movie Reviews

http://www.mrqe.com
http://www.filmcritic.com
http://www.themovieguys.com
http://www.suntimes.com/ebert/ebertser.html
If you're undecided on what movie to see, let these sites assist.

248
Where's it Playing

http://www.moviefone.com
Now that you have decided which movie you want to see, this site will tell you the times and places where it is being shown.

249
Script-O-Rama

http://www.script-o-rama.com
Drew has over 600 scripts (movie and television) that you can review.

250
Picky, Picky

http://www.nitpickers.com
Are you the kind of person who likes to find "errors of fact or omission" in movies?
Then you'll love this site; there are over 8,000 of them listed here.

251
Bloopers are Fun

http://www.moviebloopers.com
http://www.movie-mistakes.com
Actors are human. At these sites, learn about many movie bloopers and mistakes.

252
Celebrity Address Book
http://www.geocities.com/Hollywood/Hills/9842/mainframe.html
Where do over 12,000 celebrities live? Go to this address and you'll find the answers.

253
Celebrities on the Web
http://www.starbuzz.com
http://www.celebhoo.com
http://www.celebrityweb.com
http://celebritysightings.alloy.com
http://www.celebrityemail.com
Admit it, you're a stargazer. On the Web, you can look as long as you want, and no one will know you're watching.

254
I'll Wear That
http://www.asseenin.com
If you ever wanted to emulate your favorite celebrities, this site is for you. Find out what the people you admire wear and drive.

255
Hollywood Stock Exchange

http://www.hsx.com
http://www.starstock.com
Play these FANtasy games by "investing" in your favorite celebrities as if they were "shares of stock."

256
Celebrities Dead or Alive

http://www.dpsinfo.com
Remember what's-his-name? He played the in that movie with…whatever happened to him? Wonder no more. The Dead People Server lists celebrities who are long dead, newly dead or might plausibly be dead.

257
Entertainment Online

http://www.ew.com
http://www.fametracker.com
http://www.hollywood.com
http://www.showbizdata.com
Entertainment begins here.

258
I Like TV

http://www.liketelevision.com
Take a trip down memory lane. Watch Burns and Allen, The Lone Ranger, classic movies and more.

259
What's on the Tube?

http://www.tvgrid.com
Tune in to the grid, and you'll have the answer. If you're forgetful, you should sign up for its e-mail reminder service.

260
David Letterman

http://www.cbs.com/lateshow
Did you miss David's monologue last night? Hear ye, hear ye, it's on the Net.

261
Insurance Ratings

http://www.ambest.com/ratings/search.html
http://www.insureclick.com
Purchasing insurance can be confusing. These sites should insure that you get the best product for your needs.

262
Insurance Guide

http://www.insure.com
http://insurance.yahoo.com
The Yahoo! site is a comprehensive insurance center, and Insure.com says, "We inform, you decide."

263
Retirement Sounds Good

http://www.asec.org/toolshm.htm

http://www.aarp.org

Start preparing long before you retire. Thirty percent of Americans have not put money aside for their golden years. Don't be one of them.

264
Can I Help?

http://www.helping.org

http://www.allcharities.com

Donate your time or money to a worthy cause. These sites list many worthwhile organizations that could use your assistance.

265
Cars Online

http://www.autoweb.com

http://www.carsdirect.com

Tired of dealing with that car salesman in the showroom? From the comfort of your keyboard, buy your next car online.

266
Smart Lease
http://www.smartmoney.com/lease
Arm yourself with all of the details before you lease a car.

267
Auto Financing
http://www.giggocar.com
When buying a car, make an intelligent financial decision with Giggo.

268
Used Cars
http://www.autotrader.com
Buy or sell a used car online. Autotrader has over one million cars listed.

269
Used Car Appraisal
http://www.nadaguides.com
Want to know the value of a used car? Go to this handy online version of the National Appraisal Guide.

270
Everything Automotive

http://www.autopedia.com
http://www.jcwhitney.com
http://www.automobilemag.com
These sites will provide you with a comprehensive parts guide, an encyclopedia and an auto magazine.

271
Fuel Economy and Crash Tests

http://www.fueleconomy.gov
http://www.crashtest.com
How many miles to the gallon does it get, and how well has the car done in crash tests? Now, you have the answers with a click of the mouse.

272
Six Billion…

http://www.popexpo.net
http://www.pbs.org/sixbillion
…and counting. Find out lots of interesting details about the world's population.

273
Portal About Portals

http://www.traffick.com
Web sites that provide all of your information in one place have become popular. Now there is a site that reports on these portals.

274
I Did it My Way

http://www.myway.com
MyWay.com provides "a highly personalized Web portal that makes the Web more useful for everyday life."

"Hello, technical support?"

275
Let's Get Digital

http://www.kodak.com/go/play
Kodak will teach you about digital photography and help you do many fun things with your precious pictures.

276
A Century of Images

http://www.pbs.org/ktca/americanphotography
From art to cultural identity, PBS provides a creative and informative site about photography.

277
Art on the Net

http://wwar.world-arts-resources.com
If it has to do with art, you'll find it here.

278
Tattoo Art?

http://www.tattoos.com

Love 'em or hate 'em, it seems like tattoos have gone mainstream. Take a close-up look at these works of art.

279
Unique and Magnifique

http://www.bluedogart.com
http://www.threestooges.com
http://www.seinfeld.com
http://www.oprah.com

Blue Dog, the Three Stooges, Seinfeld and Oprah have all become legends in their respective fields.

280
Need a Job?

http://www.myjobsearch.com
http://www.hotjobs.com
http://www.careerbuilder.com
http://www.americasemployers.com
http://www.rileyguide.com
Need a career change? These sites will help lead you to greener pastures.

281
The National Debt

http://www.brillig.com/debt_clock
How much is the U.S. debt? Check the clock for details of this staggering sum.

282
Signature Taglines

http://www.mcs.brandonu.ca/~ennsnr/Tags/Welcome.html
Need a clever tagline for an e-mail signature? You can choose from over 290,000 possibilities at this site.

283
E-mail Cartoons
http://www.randomhouse.com/features/emailthisbook
Some people love to e-mail jokes. Here are some cartoons from "E-mail This Book."

284
Genealogy
http://www.usgenweb.org
http://www.ngsgenealogy.org
http://www.familytreemaker.com
http://www.genealogytoolbox.com
Genealogy is one of today's most popular hobbies. Use these sites to help research your ancestors.

285
Disinformation, Please
http://www.disinfo.com
We live in a world of disinformation. Find out about all that "bad info" here.

286
Real Estate Searching

http://www.realestate.com
http://realestate.yahoo.com
http://homeadvisor.msn.com
http://www.cyberhomes.com
http://www.lycos.com/realestate

Many of the search engines have gone into the real estate business. Search for your dream home here.

287
Mortgage.com

http://www.iown.com
http://www.mortgage.com

Everything from mortgage rates to the resale price of comparable homes in your neighborhood, you'll find it all at these sites.

288
On the Move

http://www.virtualrelocation.com
Are you moving sometime soon? This site can help make arranging the process
virtually pain free.

289
Buy Furniture Online?

http://www.furniture.com
http://www.furniturefind.com
Sit down, relax and purchase your furniture via the Net.

290
My Web Site

http://www.homepage.com
http://www.webmaster-resources.com
Everyone seems to have a Web site. Now you can get yours for free.

291
Dot Com

http://www.startstorm.com
http://www.networksolutions.com
Is the domain name (Web address) you want still available? This site will let you know.
If you have not yet reserved the name, click on over to Network Solutions and get it
registered for a small fee.

292
Free Web Site

http://www.beseen.com
http://www.pagetalk.com
http://www.netfreebies.net
http://www.netwhistle.com
http://www.freesitetools.com
You can use these sites to add many professional utilities to your Web site for free.
Don't pass these up.

293
Poor Richard

http://www.poorrichard.com/links
Poor Richard wants you to know everything about having a Web site. His site is rich with links to assist you.

294
Join a Community

http://www.xoom.com
http://www.tripod.com
http://www.geocities.com
Create your own Web page, join a community and find lots of other goodies at these sites. Even if you are not creating a site at this time, make sure you check these communities out.

295
My Own Store

http://store.yahoo.com
Need a Web site for your business? If you want one that requires a storefront and the ability to handle credit card transactions, here is a quick, easy and inexpensive way to get started.

296
Gizmos from Zapa

http://www.zapa.com
One of the best designed sites on the Net, Zapa allows you to place interactive, animated objects on your Web site or in your e-mail.

297
Quizzes Are Fun

http://www.coolquiz.com
All kinds of quizzes for music, quotes, TV, movies and more can be found at this very cool site.

298
Dream On

http://www.swoon.com/dream
Do you ever remember your dreams? Curious about what they might mean? This site will help you interpret what you experienced.

299
Cool Toolbar

http://www.hotbar.com
Your browser toolbar probably looks pretty boring. Spice it up at this site.

300
Tools on Your Link Bar

http://www.m-w.com
http://www.squarebox.co.uk/desktop/scalc.html
http://decoder.americom.com
http://www.anywho.com
http://www.usps.gov/ncsc/welcome1.htm
http://quote.ragingbull.com

There are many sites that make life more convenient on the Net. These are a few that I keep on my own browser link bar: dictionary, calculator, area codes, phone numbers, zip codes and real time stock quotes. I'm sure you have some of your own favorites you'd like to share. Let us know about them by voting at our Web site: http://www.300Incredible.com.

Index (by Site Number)

INDEX (BY SITE NUMBER)

INDEX (BY SITE NUMBER)

INDEX (BY SITE NUMBER)

INDEX (BY SITE NUMBER)

The Incredible Newsletter

If you are enjoying this book, you can also arrange to receive a steady stream of more "incredible Internet things," delivered directly to your e-mail address.

The Leebow Letter, Ken Leebow's weekly e-mail newsletter, provides new sites, updates on existing ones and information about other happenings on the Internet.

For more details about *The Leebow Letter* and how to subscribe, visit us at:

WWW.300INCREDIBLE.COM